Printed and Published in Great Britain by D. C. Thomson & Co., Ltd., 185 Fleet Street, London EC4A 2HS.
© D. C. Thomson & Co. Ltd., 2000. ISBN 0 85116 7349

IT'S TEACHER'S PIGEON

PECK PECK

In class IIB.

MOAN!

GROAN! WE'RE NOT WELL!

OKAY! WHAT'S WRONG?

WELL, I'VE GOT A THUMPING SORE HEAD!

HMM!

THUD THUD

COO! COO! COO! COO!

EH? PSSST! OUR PLANS TO HAVE THE DAY OFF COULD GO WRONG IF A NURSE EXAMINES US!

So—

SLOO!

SCHOOL CLINIC

BROKEN BONES

SPLINTS and THING

HOI! PESKY PIGEON!

FLAP FLAP

PLOP

FIRST ONE PLEASE!

WOW! THIS BOY HAS A DREADFUL CHILL! REST OF THE DAY OFF!

ICE LOLLY

PROD

WOW! SOME HEART BEAT! HAVE A DAY IN BED!

RAGE

BOOM

BANGA BOOM

HO-HO! I PUT 'ERBERT'S THICK GLASSES IN PLACE OF NURSE'S OWN! SHE CAN'T SEE A THING THROUGH THEM — SO THICK!

I must not give my teacher lines, I must not give my teacher lines, I must not give my teacher lines, I must not give my teacher lines, I must not give my teacher lines, I must not give my teacher lines I must not give my teacher lines, I must not give my teacher lines I must not give my teacher lines, I must not give my teacher lines

SIR! I'VE GOT A SORE ELBOW — I CAN'T DO THIS!

SIGH! SILLY BOY!

OO . . . SIR! IT MUT HAVE BEEN SOMETHING I ATE AT BREAKFAST! I DON'T FEEL WELL! CAN I GO HOME?

((GLOOP)) GLEEP BURBLE

BUMP

STOP! I'LL CHECK OUT YOUR ILLNESS! I'M GOING TO SEND FOR . . .

. . . THE SCHOOL NURSE!

LIFT

PIGEON TOE CREAM

COME TO IIB

Soon—

OKAY — LINE UP YOU SICK LOT!

OO . . . ER! WE'VE HAD IT NOW!

SPECS

CLUMP CLUMP

SLURP!

THROW

SWAP

GRRR! NO! NO! THEY'RE MAKING A FOOL OF YOU!

LEAP

CRASH

PTCHEE

WE'RE LEAVING NOW TO GET SOME FRESH AIR! JUST WHAT THE NURSE ORDERED! HA-HA-HA!

LUCKY I WAS HERE WHEN THIS ACCIDENT HAPPENED, YOU KNOW!

DOH!

TIE

I must not drive teacher up the wall.
I must not drive teacher up the wall.
I must not drive teacher up the wall.
I must not drive teacher up the wall.
I must not drive teacher up the wall.

YES, MISTER BELFRY — THE LAST TIME I VISITED THE POND IT WAS SUCH A NICE PLACE! SIGH!

ZZZZ

BASH ST. POND

But—

GAG! THIS IS THE WORST CASE OF POLLUTION I'VE EVER SEEN! PHEW!

GASP!

NASTY PLOOP

BASH ST. POND

BURBLE

WE CAN'T HAVE THIS — LET'S CLEAN UP THIS POND!

CLUNK

NNNNGH!

TUG

GRAB

AHA! THIS MYSTERIOUS STREAM MUST BE CAUSING IT!

PONG

NIFF

I'LL TAKE A SAMPLE!

WOW! WHAT STRONG STUFF! LET'S TRACE THE SOURCE OF IT!

SSSSS

SCOOP

THIS WAY!

PLEASE HAVE LUNCH ON ME! DON'T EAT ANYTHING FROM THIS KITCHEN!

EH?

SAVED US FROM SCHOOL LUNCHES! SLURP!

HOT PIZZAS

HOT PIZZAS

YAHOO!

HOP

CRANK

WONDERFUL EXAMPLES OF YET UNKNOWN SPECIES OF BACTERIA! OO...AAR!

HUH! CHEEK! PLAYING WITH 'GOOD FOOD'!

ANGLING FOR A LAUGH!

3...2...1...

TICK TOCK

1...ER...PLUS...

...HOME TIME! YAHOO!

DRING

LET'

CLAP

Suddenly—

WAA! HOW'D THEY GET INTO MY BOOTS? OOH!

WRIGGLE

TICKLE

LIVE BAIT

HA-HA! WHO KNOWS?

WHAT A SHAME — CATCHING POOR FISH!

DON'T WORRY, TOOTS. PLUG HAS GONE TO WARN THEM!

So, underwater—

SHOO!

WOW!

EEK!

But—

HUMPH! IT'S THE BRASS FISH FROM OUTSIDE THE FISH SHOP IN THE HIGH STREET! WHO COULD HAVE . . .

FISHMONGER

. . . I MIGHT HAVE KNOWN!

HA-HA! GOOD WORK, PLUG!

TUG

GRRRR!

SNIP

I must not do my homework on the school bus
I must not do my homework on the school bus
I must not do my homework on the school bus
I must not do my homework on the school bus
I must not do my homework on the school bus
must not do my homework on the school bus

ZOOM!

WOW! HE'S IN A RUSH!

CLASS IIB

FLATTEN

HUH! TEACHER'S GOING FISHING! HOW BORING!

TRA . . . LAA . . . LAA!

ZOOM

MAYBE NOT! LET'S FOLLOW HIM AND LIVEN IT UP A BIT! HAW-HAW!

Soon—

HMM! WHERE'S THE LIVE BAIT?

WHEW! WHAT AN UGLY HUMAN!

SWIM FOR IT!

ZOOM

Then—

WOW! I'VE GOT A WHOPPER!

BEND

STRAIN

IT MUST BE A RECORD CATCH!

TEE-HEE!

HEAVE

THUD

WAA!

SPIN CLICK

GOT YOU!

At Teacher's home—

WHAT ARE YOU GOING TO DO WITH YOUR PRIZE CATCH, DEAR?

I'M THINKING OF HAVING THEM PROPERLY STUFFED AND MOUNTED, MRS TEACHER!

ULP! HE IS JOKING, ISN'T HE, READERS?

CHEW

CHOMP

PRIZE CATCH

FROG CHIP SHOP

GORILLA THRILLA!

TEACHER SAID THIS WAS TO BE A SPECIAL DAY!

CLASS IIB

IT'S A SCHOOL TRIP TO BEANOTOWN SAFARI PARK!

HO-HO!

TEE-HEE!

OO... THEY'RE WILDER THAN I THOUGHT!

THE ANIMALS?

BEWARE WILD ANIMALS

SLIDE

STOP! STOP!

BOINNG

NO — THE KIDS!

GRUNT!

TAP

WAA! KING KONG!

OO... WHAT NOW?

GRAB

LIFT

GRUNT! SLURP!

WE'VE HAD IT!

OOH! THE END OF BASH STREET KIDS!

SALT PEPPER

Must not sledge on the school roof
Must not sledge on the school roof
Must not sledge on the school roof
Must not sledge on the school roof
Must not sledge on the school roof

BASH ST. SCHOOL

At the Safari Park —

NOW LINE UP AND . . .

CAR PARK

YAHOO!

TRAMPLE STOMP

. . . AAAGH!

GASP! I CAN'T CONTROL THEM!

HMM! I HAVE AN IDEA!

THWAP THWAP

DO NOT FEED THE ANIMALS

Later —

I WONDER WHAT WE'LL FIND HERE?

BUMP

OOF! A HAIRY TREE!

HO-HO! IT'S NOT A REAL GORILLA! IT'S A HUGE MODEL WE'RE ABLE TO WORK FROM IN HERE! THE PARK RANGERS LENT IT TO US TO GIVE THE KIDS A FRIGHT!

OPEN

OO . . . ER!

GROWL! GRUNT!

WAH!

OOH!

WHO WANTS TO BE A MILLIONAIRE?

I DO!

I'D LOVE TO BE IN THE SPOTLIGHT.

pay SPOTTY £1,000,000

AND I'VE ALWAYS WANTED A SOUPED-UP SPOTS CAR.

POSH CAR SHOWROOM

SPOT 1

I'D GET THE RED SPOTTED CARPET TREATMENT WHEREVER I WENT.

HOTEL SWANKO

OF COURSE, I'D NEED A SPOTTER PLANE TO GO HOUSE-HUNTING.

WAHEY! THERE IT IS — HOME SPOTTY HOME!

FOR SALE SPOTTY TOWERS

GARLIC PONG!

PARENTS PENDING

I'VE DECIDED TO HAVE A PARENTS' DAY TODAY. PUPILS CAN INVITE THEIR PARENTS TO COME ALONG AND DISCUSS PROBLEMS THEY MAY HAVE WITH THEIR CHILDREN'S EDUCATION. I THINK IT'S RATHER A GOOD IDEA!

WAA!

YAHOO!

TRAMPLE CRUSH

HOWL

I HAVE TO COMPLAIN ABOUT MY 'ERBERT'S HEAVY JOTTER!

EH?

'ERBERT'S MUM ↓

THIS THICK PAPER MAKES HOLES IN HIS POCKETS!

HO-HO! 'ERBERT MUST HAVE MISSED HIS JOTTER AND WRITTEN ON HIS DESK LID!

THUD

2+2 = 2½%¾ 7⅓⅔% 5 × 3 = Dunno

ER . . . CARE TO LOOK OVER YOUR SON'S WORK BOOKS PERHAPS?

CHOMP! OKAY!

CHEW! MUNCH!

FATTY'S PARENTS

FATTY'S JOTTER

FATTY'S JOTTER

WAA! THEY'RE ONLY AFTER MY 'PLAYTIME SNACK'!

OOPS!

CHOMP! MUNCH! GUZZLE!

FATTY'S DESK

WHY DON'T YOU MAKE USE OF OUR DAUGHTER'S MUSICAL TALENTS?

EH? WHAT DOES SHE PLAY? PERHAPS SHE COULD HAVE A PLACE IN THE SCHOOL ORCHESTRA?

↙ TOOTS'S PARENTS

SHE PLAYS THE GHETTO BLASTER!

YEAH! YEAH!

SNAP SNAP

BOOM BOOM BANGA

BOOM BOOM BOOM

EEK!

GENERATING ELEC-TRICKERY!

SIGH! WE HATE SCHOOL!

GLOOM!

GLOOM!

MOAN! MUTTER!

EVEN MORE GLOOM!

HUMPH!

NO — WE HAVE A GENERATOR IN THE BASEMENT. GO AND SEE IF YOU CAN GET IT STARTED!

OKAY, YOUR HEADSHIP!

AW! BOO!

So, in the basement—

HMM! IT'S RUN ON OIL BUT WE DON'T HAVE ANY LEFT!

HURRAY!

OIL HERE

PLEASE, SIR! I CAN CONVERT IT TO RUN ON SOMETHING OTHER THAN OIL!

BOO! HISS!

SIMPER! WONDERFUL PUPIL! GET TO WORK!

PAT! PAT!

CUTHBERT CRINGEWORTHY SCHOOL SWOT

HEH-HEH! OUR FIVE FOOT MOUSE!

YUM! PIE! DROOL!

ZOOM!

THREE CHEERS FOR OUR BRIGHTEST PUPIL! HIP, HIP . . .

CLICK! SPIN

SLURP!

CLICK!

BOO!

VERY BRIGHT

RIGHT! ON WITH THE LESSONS!

PUFF! PANT! WHEEZE! DROOL!

VROOM!

ZOOM!

BY LOOK OR BY CROOK!

SCHOOL KITCHEN

AHA! OLIVE'S COOKING LUNCH, I SEE.

Within the mist —

WE'RE LOST!

POLICE VAN

HMM!

Shortly —

ER — THIS IS A STICK-UP. HAND OVER YOUR LOOT.

CHOMP!

JELLY BABIES

TUT! TUT! THAT'S NOT HOW YOU DO A HOLD-UP. YOU MUST USE A MASK.

LIKE THIS, YOU MEAN? THIS IS A HOLD-UP!

JELLY BABIES

GASP! THE YOUTH OF TODAY. SIGH!

Then —

TEACHER! THERE'S A CROOK IN THE AREA. BE ON YOUR GUARD.

IT'S HIM — THE ESCAPED CROOK.

ERK! MUST THINK FAST!

STAY BACK OR THESE KIDS GET SPLATTERED.

SNATCH!

I'M TAKING THE KIDS HOSTAGE. I CAN STAY LOCKED UP IN THIS KITCHEN FOR AGES.

STRETCH

KITCHEN

GASP!

I must not hide among the school gargoyles
I must not hide among the school gargoyles
I must not hide among the school gargoyles
I must not hide among the school gargoyles

I'LL ESCAPE WHILE THEY TRY TO FIND OUT WHERE THEY ARE.

POLICE VAN

CLICK!

AHA! I'LL GET A DISGUISE IN HERE

SCHOOL LOST PROPERTY

LEAP!

Soon —

NOW TO JOIN THIS CLASS. HEH-HEH!

CLASS IIB

TAKE YOUR SEATS. OH! A NEW BOY.

AHEM! YES, SIR!

CLASS IIB

THE CROOK WOULD HAVE A PROBLEM PINCHING MY WALLET WITHOUT ME KNOWING IT.

EH?

WALLET

IT HAS A BELL ON IT — OW!

DING! DING!

NO CHANCE OF GETTING YOUR WALLET.

WALLET

TUG!

CHORTLE! NO BELLS ON YOUR TROUSERS, THOUGH!

EEK!

EH?

THIS COULD BE VERY DANGEROUS, HEADMASTER.

KITCHEN

HORRIBLE NIFF!

I'M AWARE OF THAT . . .

KITCHEN

. . . BUT I DON'T THINK THE KIDS WILL HARM THAT POOR CROOK TOO MUCH. HA-HA-HA!

COME ON — EAT OLIVE'S FOOD.

MERCY! MERCY! LET ME BACK TO NICE PRISON! PLEASE! PRETTY PLEASE! I WON'T BE NAUGHTY AGAIN!

SPLUTTER!

ZOOM!

IT'S A FUNNY OLD GAME!

GRRR! GET INTO SCHOOL!

SWISH!
CLUMP!

TRAMPLE!
SQUASH!
EH? WHO'S THAT?

TRING! TRING!

CLASS II B

AHEM! SOME DIFFERENT GAMES TO STUDY HERE — I'D SAY!

WHAT GAME ARE YOU PLAYING?

NOT STANDING ON THE CRACKS GAME!

BUT THERE AREN'T ANY CRACKS AT ALL!

FLAP! FLAP!

But—

NOT SO FAST, TOOTS!

SNIP!

EEK!

ZONK!

OOF!

AND WHAT GAMES DID YOU TWO PLAY AT SCHOOL?

TWEET! TWEET!

DANNY WILFRID SIDNEY SMIFFY FATTY TOOTS TEACHER

PUBLIC OUTRAGE

WHAT'S GOING ON TODAY?

PUFF PANT

BASH STREET SCHOOL

RUB

SWEEP

POLISH

Suddenly —

RUMBLE

ROLL

AAAGH! SQUASH

DON'T JUST LIE THERE — GET UP AND GET READY FOR OUR VISITORS!

EH?

VISITORS?

WE'RE GOING TO OPEN TO THE PUBLIC. I'M EXPECTING LOTS OF TOURISTS TODAY!

SCHOOL

PLOP

HA-HA!

CASH

Suddenly —

VROOM

SCREECH

TAKE COVER — HERE THEY COME!

OO...ER...THANKS!

HO-HO! WE'D BETTER SEE WHAT THE TOURISTS ARE UP TO!

DOH!

WELCOME

In class —

SMILE!

CHEESE!

FLASH

CLICK

FLASH

YUM!

NO...NO...NO!

CUT! CUT!

EH?

MATHS

WHO WANTS TO BE A MILLIONAIRE!

THE **BASH STREET KIDS** in **SCHOOL TWINNERS**

ALL ABOARD! WE'VE BEEN TWINNED WITH A FOREIGN SCHOOL — NOW WE'RE OFF TO VISIT THEM.

FANCY PLUG HAVING A TWIN.

MAYBE IT'LL BE IN SPAIN.

SNORT

IT COULD BE FRANCE.

BLAT TWANG

OR MADEIRA. SCHOOL THERE WOULD BE A PIECE OF CAKE.

CHOMP GUZZLE

MADEIRA SCHOOL

I'D TAKE TO VENICE LIKE A DUCK TO WATER.

GRAND CANAL

ZOOM!

SWOOSH!

SPLASH!

Hours later —

ICY BLAST

BRR! SHUT THAT WINDOW.

ALMOST THERE, KIDS.

WELCOME TO GLEN BASH STREET THE NOO!

SCOTLAND!?!

COME ALONG. THE SCHOOL'S ONLY THREE MILES UP THIS TRACK.

GROAN!

TEACHER MUST THINK WE'RE HEAD CASES.

OO-ER! MUST BE THE LEGENDARY SCOTCH MIST.

The BASH STREET KIDS in RUNNING RIOT

COO! TEACHER'S PUTTING UP A NOTICE.

MAYBE WE'RE GETTING AN EXTRA HOLIDAY.

VOLUNTEERS WANTED FOR

UNRAVEL

OR BIGGER HELPINGS AT SCHOOL DINNERS.

OR NEW SPOTTY BLAZERS.

RUB!

AAH! AN INSTANT RUNNING TEAM — SPLENDID!

VOLUNTEERS WANTED FOR BASH STREET HARRIERS RUNNING TEAM

— SEE TEACHER

GASP! NO WAY.

I JUST LIKE RUNNY CUSTARD!

BASH STREET SCHOOL

WE'RE RUNNING ALL RIGHT — RUNNING AWAY.

ZOOM

CACKLE! I'LL HARRY THE LITTLE HARRIERS WITH MY CAR.

SWOT

THUD

POUND

And so —

BEANO TOWN PARK

RIGHT, FIVE LAPS OF THE PARK — GET GOING!

SLAVE DRIVER!

AND THAT DOESN'T INCLUDE LAPPING ICE CREAM, FATTY.

BUT IT'S FOR ENERGY, SIR.

SNATCH. LAP. LAP.

I'LL JUST FEED THE DUCKS WHILE THE YOUNG RASCALS SUFFER. CHORTLE!

FATTY'S CONFISCATED SANDWICHES

ZONK

Shortly —

PUFF!

PUFF!

AAH! THAT MUST BE THEM BACK ALREADY.

PUFFING BILLY

COACH TWO

HO-HO! TEACHER CAN'T SAY WE'RE NOT IN TRAINING!

PUFF! PUFF!

GROOGH!

SPLASH

PUFFING BILLY

BILLY CAN DO OUR PUFFING FOR US.

ZOOM!

BUMP

LOOKS LIKE TEACHER'S OUT OF HIS DEPTH AS A TRAINER.

SNORT! GERROFF MY TRAIN.

OUR SHOES ARE WRECKED.

WE CAN'T DO THAT RUN NOW.

HMM! UPON MY SOLE! I'VE HAD A BRAINWAVE.

That night —

YAWN! JOLLY TIRING DAY I'VE HAD.

OO-ER! SHE'S NOT SOUNDING TOO HEALTHY.

RUMBLE   CLUNK!

QUIET!

UGH! SOMEBODY'S PINCHED MY TYRES.

KLUNK!

THAT BASH STREET LOT ARE GOING FOR A SPRINT!

YOU CAN'T SPRINT A MARATHON.

13

JUST MAKING SOME FINAL ADJUSTMENTS TO OUR RUNNING SHOES.

SQUEEZE

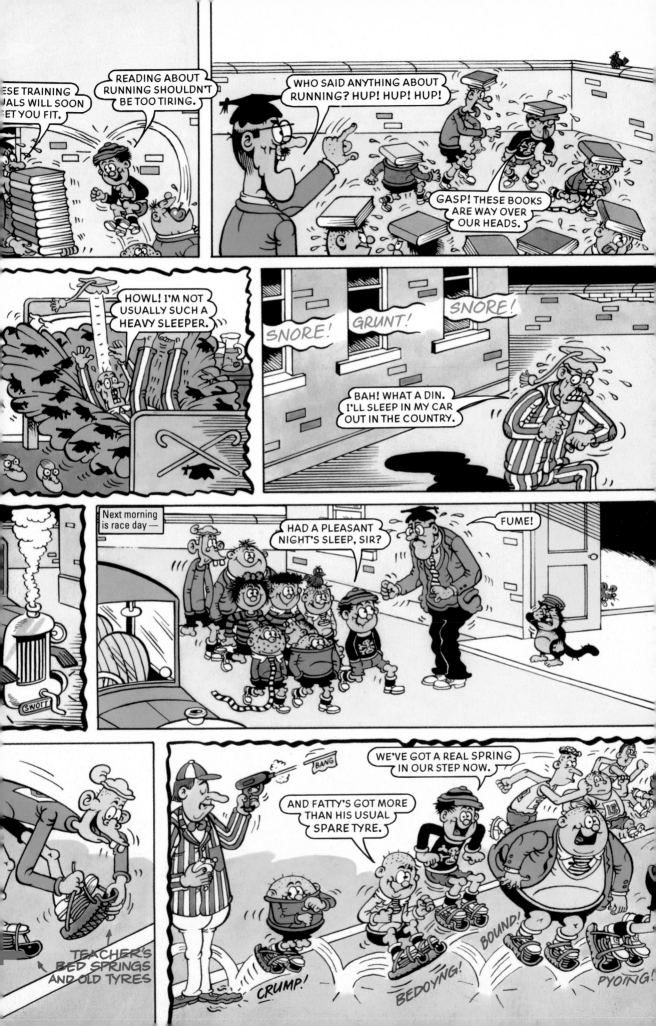

WHO WANTS TO BE A MILLIONAIRE?

I DO!

I'D BOOK MYSELF INTO A PRIVATE CLINIC FOR A GOOD GOING OVER.

POSH PRIVATE CLINIC

SWANK!

DRIBBLE! SWOON!

DROOL!

£1,000,000

RECEPTION

I'D HAVE MY TEETH REDUCED.

OPERATING THEATRE

GRIND!

SKREEK!

HAIR RESTORER

MY EARS TAKEN IN AND GET A FULL HEAD OF HAIR.

GREAT TO WALK DOWN THE STREET WITH A TOTALLY DIFFERENT FACE.

PITY IT'S NOT DIFFERENT FROM DENNIS, THOUGH.

GRR! THIS TOWN'S ONLY BIG ENOUGH FOR ONE MENACE.

JUNIOR JANITORS

Before 9 o'clock —

BOILER ROOM

SNAP

TRUNDLE

WAA!

TRIP

AND YOU'LL NOT HAVE TO DO ANY HOMEWORK FOR A MONTH!

OKAY!

Soon —

I SAID I'D SWEEP UP AND TIDY . . .

IN HERE! YUM, CHOMP! GUZZLE!

SWEEP

SCHOOL KITCHEN

In the janitor's office —

YUM! TEABREAK TIME!

GYM DOOR KEY

BISCUIT STORE KEY

FRONT DOOR KEY

GRAB

SLURP!

In the biscuit store.

THIS IS THE LIFE! CHOMP!

CRUNCH!

CREAM PUFFS

TOFFEE BICCIES

WAFER BICCIES

POUR

TEA

CHOCCY BICCIES

CHOCCY B

CREAM BICCIES

DIGESTIVES

GASP! WHAT'S BEEN GOING ON?

RESERVED FOR TEACHER

RESERVED FOR HEAD

Must not act the fool in class. Must not act the fool in class. Must not act the fool in class
Must not act the fool in class. Must not act the fool in class. Must not act the fool in class
Must not act the fool in class. Must not act the fool in class. Must not act the fool in class
Must not act the fool in class. Must not act the fool in class. Must not act the fool in class

WOW!

TOPPLE

BUMP

AAAGH!

Soon —

WHAT'LL WE DO NOW? THE SCHOOL CAN'T FUNCTION WITHOUT A JANITOR! OH, SIGH!

BOILER

Later —

HOW'D YOU LIKE TO HELP OUT WITH THE JANITOR'S DUTIES?

NOT A CHANCE!

ZOOM

WE'RE PUTTING OUT WASTE-PAPER FOR COLLECTION!

PUSH

BASH STREET SCHOOL

CHORTLE!

SCHOOL BOOKS

ENGLISH

MATHS

SCHOOL REFUSE

SCHOOL REFUSE

TRUNDLE

EEK!

WOW!

SPLAT

SPLAT

SUPER LINE

I'M JUST MARKING OUT A NETBALL COURT, DANNY!

YES — SUPER IDEA OF MINE — KIDS DOING JANITOR'S DUTIES!

SNARL!

GLOO

Then —

OUT! OUT! YOU'RE NOT NEEDED NOW!

EH? CHEW!

CHOC BISC

MIL CHOC

I'VE GOT THE PERFECT PART-TIME REPLACEMENT! TITTER!

2 7 5 | 1 6 8

CHOMP! CRUNCH!

THROW

SWEEP

SLURP!

ROOM FOR IMPROVEMENT

THIS IS MR MATT E. MULSION...

VERY KEEN ON HIS JOB

ROLL

UNDER-COAT

...HE'S COME TO VARNISH THE CLASSROOM FLOOR!

TUM-TEE-TUM

DAB

DAB

PLUG'S FACE WORKS BETTER THAN ANY HEAT GUN!

BLISTER   BUBBLE

NOW WE NEED TO SAND THE FLOOR!

NO PROBLEM!

ZOOM

THERE YOU ARE!

POUR   SAND

SILLY, SILLY BOY!

DON'T WORRY — I'LL GET THE FLOOR SANDED!

WAHEY!

SLIDE

RUMBLE

HOI!

SPLASH   ZOOM

ER — MR MULSION, COULD I ORDER SOME WALLPAPER?

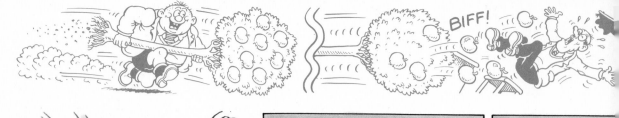

ORCHESTRAL MANOEUVRES

TEACHER TOLD US TO BE AT THE TOWN HALL AT TEN O'CLOCK FOR THE BEANO TOWN ORCHESTRA COMPETITION. A CHANCE TO USE OUR NEW DIGITAL WATCHES!

TICK! ROLL! TICK!

SEEN MY NEW WATER-PISTOL, KIDS! HAW-HAW!

SWOO

SQUEE

OO-ER! WE'RE TRAPPED — UNLESS . . .

. . . HANDY THING A TROMBONE!

SWING!

SPIN!

HEH-HEH!

GNASH, GNASH!

THERE'S DAD. HE'S GOT A PART TIME JOB AS A LOLLIPOP MAN!

CHILDREN STOP CROSSING

PURR!

NATTER! NATTER!

GOOD TO SEE YOU, DAD. GOT TO GO NOW!

CHILDREN STOP CROSSING

HEY, 'ERBERT — I DON'T THINK YOU'LL PLAY MUCH WITH THAT!

CHILDREN STOP CROSSING

Meanwhile —

I Must not bring teacher an apple every day
I Must not bring teacher an apple every day
I Must not bring teacher an apple every day
I Must not bring teacher an apple every day
I Must not bring teacher an apple every day

MUST GET REVENGE!

POUR!

LIKE OUR WATER CANNON, DENNIS?

SWOOSH!

GLOOP!

OOPS! THAT HASN'T DONE A LOT FOR MY INSTRUMENT

BLOOP!

GURGLE!

OH, NO! GNASHER'S NOT TOO PLEASED THAT WE SOAKED HIS MASTER!

ZOOM!

THUNK!

PING!

BANG! BANG! BANG! BANG! BANG!

YEEHA! GOT YA!

CORKS

MINNIE THE MINX

READY, INJUNS?

STRETCH!

ERM . . .

STRETCH!

YEEOWP!

THUD!

SNAP!

TWANG!

TWANG!

YAP!

PTCHEE!

SNAP!

TWANG!

TWANG!

YOU'RE HERE ON TIME — BUT WHERE ARE YOUR INSTRUMENTS?

ER — WE HAD A FEW PROBLEMS.

TOWN HALL

But soon —

WE WON THE NOVELTY SECTION.

BUT, HOW!

RING-A-TING!

FOR OUR UNIQUE DIGITAL WATCH BAND!

JUDGE

THE TRAIN TAKES THE STRAIN

TO ART CLASS

TIME FOR THE ART LESSON. UP TO THE CLASS, KIDS!

YAHOO!

PHEW! PUFF!

ZOOM

Later, downstairs.

HMM!

BANG

THUD

THUMP

Soon —

THERE — TRAINS TO GET YOU AROUND IN SCHOOL, GENTS!

COO!

BATTERY POWERED

HEH-HEH!

RUMBLE

GUARD'S VAN

FATTY'S IN THE BUFFET CAR!

HUH! I MIGHT HAVE KNOWN!

MUNCH! CHOMP!

SPIN

SPIN

THIS IS WHERE . . .

. . . WE PART!

CLICK

SLOW DOWN

JUMP! JUMP! JUMP!

I must not put jumping beans down teacher's underpants
I must not put jumping beans down teacher's underpants
I must not put jumping beans down teacher's underpants
I must not put jumping beans down teacher's underpants
I must not put jumping beans down teacher's underpants
I must not put jumping beans down teacher's underpants

HA! TOO MANY STEPS, TEACHER?

GASP! WHEEZE!

ART CLASS

Later —

WHEEZE! PUFF!

PHEW! PUFF! MUST BE AN EASIER WAY TO GET AROUND SCHOOL!

I HAVE AN IDEA, SIR!

ART CLASS

PLANS

WE MADE THIS TUNNEL, SIR!

IT'S A GHOST TRAIN RIDE! HO-HO!

WAA!

(RUMBLE)

Then —

FUNNY — NO POWER TO GET UPSTAIRS!

SLOW DOWN

AHA! WE SEE WHAT'S WRONG!

IT'S THE BEST WAY, READERS! YOU SEE . . .

ZOOM

STOP

. . . SMIFFY'S IN THE SIGNAL BOX!

ZOOM

2 x 3 =

TUG

SPIN

OO . . . ER! I HOPE I'VE GOT THIS RIGHT!

SIGNAL BOX

WAH!

WHIRR

CLICK

EEK!

ZOOM

CLUNK

SPIN

RUMBLE

A GAME OF PATIENCE

PATIENCE IS SOMETHING SHOWN WHILE, FOR INSTANCE, WAITING IN A QUEUE OR FORMING A LINE!

PATIENCE

LIKE ANTS, SIR! THEY'RE GOOD AT FORMING LINES!

GASP! A SENSIBLE THO FROM A DIM PUPIL! W MADE YOU THINK OF

COME BACK AFTER LUNCH WITH EXAMPLES OF 'PATIENCE'. SEE IF YOU CAN FIND QUEUES OF PEOPLE!

ZOOM

CHORTLE! OKAY!

Soon —

TONI'S FISH & CHIPS

CLOSED

EASY QUEUE TO FIND — I'M IN IT EVERY DAY!

COME AND GET IT!

FISH AND CHIP SMELL

OPEN

YUM! DROOL!

ZOOM

CLOSED

SORRY! H BOUGHT THE

AND HOW LONG HAVE YOU BEEN WAITING FOR A BUS?

OH, NO!

OUR BUS!

GO BY BUS

'ULP! MISSED IT WHILE TALKING TO US!

VROOM

ZOOM

SNARL! TWO HOURS TILL NEXT ONE!

BACK TO SCHOOL, PLUG — AT THE DOUBLE!

ZOOM

I must knuckle down in class. I must knuckle down in class
I Must knuckle down in class. I must knuckle down in class
I Must knuckle down in class. I must knuckle down in class
I Must knuckle down in class. I must knuckle down in class
I Must knuckle down in class. I must knuckle down in class
I Must knuckle down in class. I must knuckle down in class

GUEST APPEARANCE FROM ...
LORD SNOOTY
THANK YOU, SCRAPPER.
YOUR LANCE, YOUR LORDSHIP!

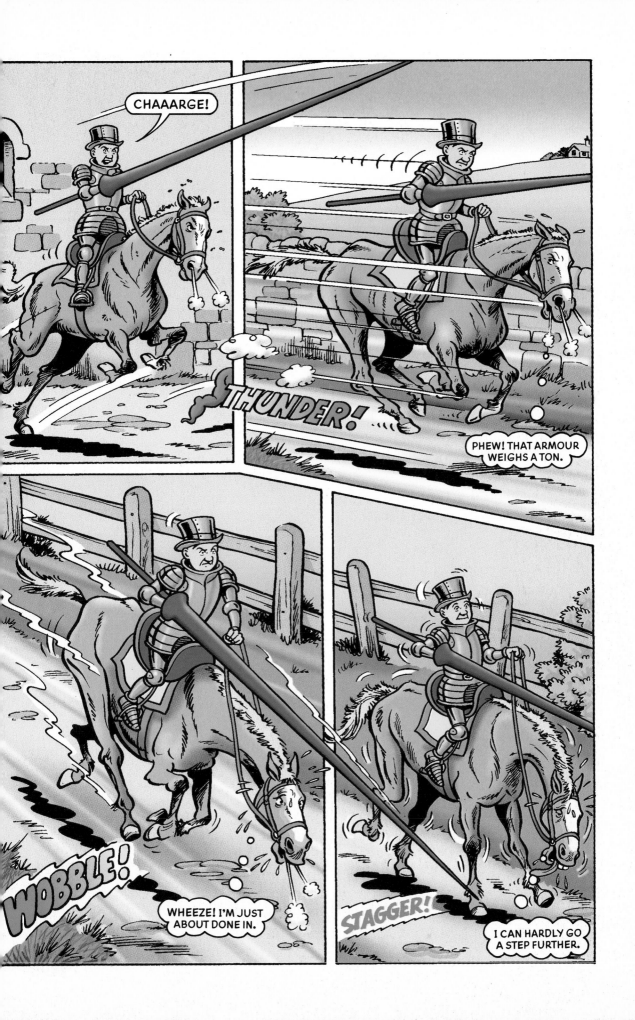

WHO WANTS TO BE A MILLIONAIRE?

WHAT ARE YOU DOING, TOOTS?

POUR!

I JUST WANTED THE FREE PLASTIC KNIGHT YOU GET WITH THIS CEREAL!

GRAB

POUR!

RIGHT, WI UP YOU C

So —

ROLL UP — A FREE PARTY HAT TO ALL THOSE WHO HAVE LUNCH!

LUNCH HALL

FLOP!

OLIVE

FREE GIFTS

Soon —

THANKS FOR THE HATS, OLIVE!

REE IFTS

THEY SAVED US HAVING TO EAT THIS GHASTLY FOOD!

EEK!

FREE GIFTS

SHAKE!

SHAKE!

And —

WAH!

FLOATAWAY!

'BYE-'BYE!

MAYBE WE SHOULD GIVE SOMETHING FREE TO THE BASH STREET FANS!

WE DO — EVERY WEEK!

WE GIVE THE READERS TWO FREE STAPLES IN OUR PAGE EACH WEEK!

I must not fidget in class. I must not fidget in class
I must not fidget in class. I must not fidget in class
I must not fidget in class. I must not fidget in class
I must not fidget in class. I must not fidget in class
I must not fidget in class. I must not fidget in class
I must not fidget in class. I must not fidget in class

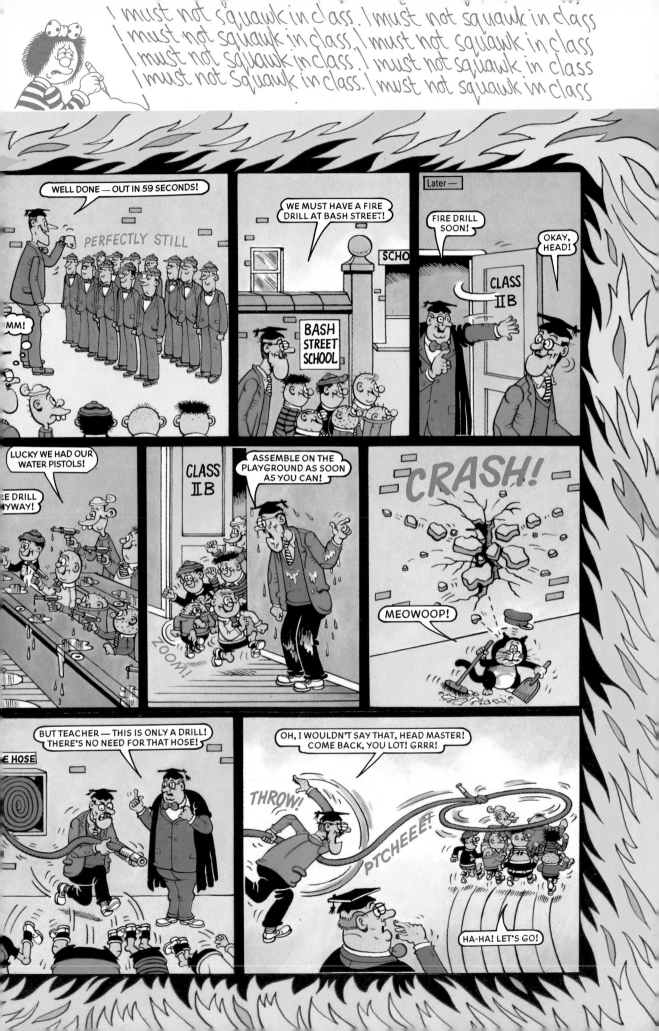

ONE FAT DINNER LADY

The first ice-cream soda was served in Philadelphia in 1874. It's still one of America's most popular soda-fountain specials.

For a "Black and White" soda, so called because of the chocolate syrup base and vanilla ice-cream, in a tall glass mix ¼ cup milk with 3 tablespoons chocolate syrup. Add 1 cup soda water, or flavoured soft drink, and 2 scoops vanilla ice-cream. Top with whipped cream and add a straw. Experiment with other flavours.

THE CLASSIC BACON CHEESEBURGER.

A juicy grilled burger covered with America Cheddar and topped with crispy bacon slice makes a hearty choice.

Toast a *sesame seed hamburger bun.* Just before the hamburger is done, cover with a *slice of Cheddar cheese* and continue cooking until cheese begins to melt. Place on bottom of bun, cover with *crispy bacon slices* and top half of bun. Serve with *ketchup, mustard* and *relishes* and lots of *French fries.*

FRENCH TOAST. OOH LA LA!

At home and in restaurants, French toast is a popular breakfast dish made from bread dipped in an egg-and-milk mixture; fried in butter; served with syrup or sugar.

Dip a slice of white bread into a batter made from 2 eggs, ¼ cup milk, 1 tablespoon sugar and dash of salt. Coat well and lightly fry in butter until browned on both sides.

Try adding flavourings to batter such as ground cinnamon or nutmeg, vanilla or almond extract, grated orange or lemon peel; serve with a variety of syrups, honey, jams and preserves.

COOL IT, CHILLED-REN!

WHAT'S THIS?

ERK!

TUG!

WHAT ABOUT THE LACK OF HEATING, JANITOR!

BOILER ROOM

BOILER ROOM

BOILER ROOM

IT'S NOT MY FAULT! I ONLY GET ONE LUMP OF COAL AND TWO LOLLY-STICKS TO BURN EACH MONTH!

BRRRR!

COAL

BOILER

THEN I SHALL HAVE WORDS WITH THE HEADMASTER!

. . . NOT ONLY DOES THIS KEEP YOU COSY — BUT IT'S JUST THE PLACE TO DIP YOUR BISCUIT! YUM!

GASP! THANK YOU, HEADMASTER!

YEUCH!

GROO!

DIP!

SPOOSH!

SIGH! I'M WARMER IN MY LITTLE CAR!

HMM!

Later —

THERE, SIR! WE PUSHED YOUR CAR INTO CLASS. YOU CAN SIT INSIDE AND KEEP WARM!

EEK! ER . . . HOW KIND!

WAA!

SPIN!

...S ...EACHER!

BRR! IT'S COLD IN SCHOOL! CHECK THE THERMOMETER!

FLAP!

FLAP!

KNOCK

I CAN'T TELL, SIR! TOO MUCH ICE ON IT!

BLOW!

WHEW! I'LL HAVE TO HAVE A WORD WITH THE JANITOR!

WE'RE FEELING THE COLD, HEADMASTER!

BEANO

YOU ARE A FOOL

KNEEL HERE

I HAVE AN EASY WAY TO KEEP WARM. I'LL GIVE YOU ALL A TIP!

WHILE WEARING BIKE CLIPS, FILL YOUR TROUSERS WITH NICE WARM TEA . . .

HA-HA! WE CAN'T HEAR A WORD TEACHER'S SAYING!

MUMBLE! MUMBLE!

MATHS

CHORTLE! AND HIS WINDOWS ARE FROSTING UP SO TEACHER CAN'T SEE TOO CLEARLY WHAT WE'RE DOING!

ZOOM!

PUSH!

CRASH!

MURFLE!

ZOOM!

OLD CANES

3×3

SLIDE

CRASH!

BANGERS 'N' BASH!

SNIFF! SNIFF! YUM!

FATTY'S VERY KEEN TO GET TO SCHOOL!

AFTER HIM — THERE'S SOMETHING WRONG!

SNIFF!

BA... STR... SCHO...

But —

OH, NO!

YUM! BURP! THEY WERE GREAT!

SNATCH!

CLASS II B

OTHER MEMBERS OF OUR SOCIETY ARE VISITING BEANOTOWN! I'LL INVITE THEM INTO SCHOOL TO GIVE YOU A TALK ON RARE SAUSAGES!

BAM!

PHOO!

So later —

HOW DO?

THIS IS MISTER A. BANGER AND MISTER B. LINK!

← SAUSAGE SUIT

MR B. LINK

...GER

In the school kitchen —

YUM! SOON BE READY!

SIZZLE!

Then —

SCHOOL KITCHEN

DROOL! DO I SMELL LUNCH? YUMMY!

ER... HEADMASTER!

I'LL HAVE SOME OF THIS LOVELY SAUSAGE!

EEK! N... NOT YE...

SIZZLE!

SSS

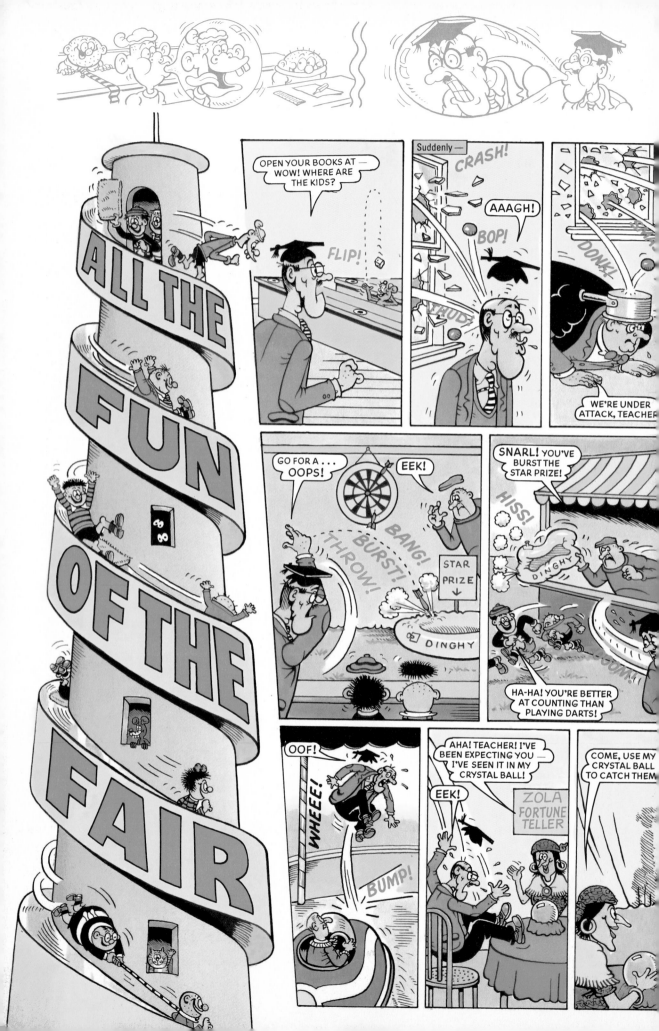

...ONLY A FAIR NEXT TO BASH STREET SCHOOL! SOME PEOPLE AT THE COCONUT SHY CAN'T THROW STRAIGHT! I BET THAT'S WHERE I'LL FIND THE KIDS!

At the fair —

SIR! SIR! WE NEED YOUR HELP!

AHA!

WE HAVE TO SCORE OVER 50 TO WIN A PRIZE!

ONE DART LEFT BUT WE DON'T KNOW WHAT TO AIM FOR!

WE CAN'T COUNT UP THAT FAR!

GIVE ME THE DART!

HMM! THEY'RE IN A CAR WHICH IS VERY LIKE MY OWN DEAR LITTLE CAR!

THIS IS YOUR CAR, TEACHER! THOSE LITTLE DODGEMS WOULDN'T HOLD FATTY!

OOH!

OO... I CAN'T LOOK!

CRASH!

C'MERE!

LEAP!

LOOK OUT!

OKAY — I WILL!

EEK!

WOW!

THROW!

BOWL!

But —

EH? WHAT?

HAR-HAR! NO SCHOOLING FOR US TODAY ANYWAY!

SCHOOL CLOSED

DODGEMS FOR ME!

ME FIRST ON THE BIG WHEEL!

YAHOO! LET'S GO TO THE FAIR!

WHO WANTS TO BE A MILLIONAIRE?

A GOLF TEE-HEE!

DRING DRING

YAHOO! GOING HOME TIME!

But — GANGWAY!

ZOOM

STOMP

EH! GASP! TEACHER'S IN A HURRY!

So —

SWISH SWISH

WHACK

DO YOUR STUFF, SID!

CHIRP! TWEET! TWEET! CHIRPY! TWEET!

PTCHEE

HA-HA! HE'S GIVING HIS PET INSTRUCTIONS!

GRAB

YIKES!

PULL DOWN

WAP!

YOU MISSED IT! I'VE WON! I'M THE MAN! YAHOO!

CHORTLE!

GNASH! GNNNN!

BITE

TEACHER'S

THIS IS A CLUE TO THE SUBJECT OF TODAY'S LESSON. ANY GUESSES?

THE CHARGE OF THE LIGHT BRIGADE, SIR. HOW WHIMSICAL!

GROAN!

Class swot.

SLAP! SLAP! SLAP!

LET US BEGIN! ON ONE SIDE OF THE VALLEY THE BRITISH TROOPS WERE COMMANDED BY THE EARL OF SANDWICH AND . . .

. . . WHAT SO FUNNY

BONK!

COULD WE PLEASE CONTINUE WITH THE LESSON?

ER . . . OKAY!

NOW, ON THE OTHER SIDE OF THE VALLEY, THE BRITISH TROOPS WERE COMMANDED BY . . .

. . . LORD CARDIGAN!

WHOOAAA HA! HA! HA! HA! HA! HA! HA! HA!

HA! HA! HA! HA!

OKAY! THAT'S ENOUGH!

ONE MORE SOUND OUT OF ANYONE AND YOU'LL ALL GET EXTRA WORK AFTER SCHOOL!

MUFFLED TITTERS.

WHEW! THAT'S BETTER.

I must not scare the mirror in the school toilet
I must not scare the mirror in the school toilet
I must not scare the mirror in the school toilet
I must not scare the mirror in the school toilet

LOSING BATTLE

SORRY, TEACHER . . . HA! HA!

. . . IT WAS THE THOUGHT OF THE BRITISH TROOPS COMMANDED BY A SANDWICH!

LOOK! FATTY'S JUST EATEN THE BRITISH COMMANDER.

CHOMP!

IMAGINE BEING NAMED AFTER A CARDIGAN! HA! HA! HA! HA! HA! HA! HA!

IN FACT, THE CARDIGAN WAS NAMED AFTER HIM!

WHY? WAS HE THICK AND WOOLLY?

GRRRR!

HA! HA! HA! HA! HA! HA! HA! HA! HA! HA! HA! HA! HA! HA! HA! HA! HA! HA! HA! HA! HA! HA! HA!

STOMP! STOMP! STOMP!

HA-HA-HA! A SANDWICH! HO-HO-HO!

THAT DOES IT! EXTRA WORK FOR EVERYONE!

SLAP! SLAP! SLAP!

HA-HA-HA! THICK AND WOOLLY! HEE-HEE!

Just got the joke.

THANKS, SMIFFY! HUMPH!

SEA LIFE CENTRE

HOBBY HORSEPLAY

WHY AREN'T YOU GETTING READY FOR THE KIDS ARRIVING AT SCHOOL, TEACHER?

I FEEL IT'S GOING TO BE A GOOD DAY! THE KIDS ARE EACH GIVING A TALK ON THEIR HOBBIES! THEY SEEMED VERY KEEN!

Suddenly —

TITTER! SILLY MAN!

CRUMP!

HA-HA! ERBERT MISSED THE BLOCK OF WOOD!

AAGH! MY DESK!

. . . UNTIL I FINISH!

Next —

BOOM BADOOM! -DOOM DABOOM!

MY HOBBY'S DISCO DANCING!

SNAP! SNAP! SNAP!

NO, SIR! THESE ARE FOR MY HOBBY — ESCAPOLOGY! ESCAPING FROM THINGS!

THROW!

CLANG!

CLUNK!

FLATTEN!

HUH! BUT FAKE CHAINS ARE USED!

NO, SIR! LOOK . . .

. . . AND REAL PADLOCKS!

HUH! I DON'T THINK SO!

TUG!

CHINK!

I must not get help to write my lines. I must not get help to write my lines I must not get help to write my lines. I must not get help to write my lines must not get help to write my lines. I must not get help to write my lines must not get help to write my lines. I must not get help to write my lines must not get help to write my lines. I must not get help to write my lines

AAARGH!

In class —

WHO'LL GIVE THEIR HOBBY TALK FIRST?

ME...ME!

MY HOBBY IS WOOD CARVING! I'LL DEMONSTRATE AS I TALK BY MAKING A HOUSE OUT OF THIS BLOCK OF WOOD!

FIRST OF ALL I CUT A BIT FROM HERE... AND...THERE...

WAH! MY POOR EARS!

AW! THE ONLY PROBLEM IS THE BATTERIES ONLY LAST TWO MINUTES!

PHEW! PITY! AHEM!

CLICK!

WAA! A GHOST!

RATTLE!

CHINK!

CLANG!

I AM A GOOD ESCAPOLOGIST...

CLICK!

CLICK!

...JUST WATCH ME ESCAPE FOR THE REST OF THE DAY. HA-HA!

GRRR! COME BACK! SNARL!

YAHOO!

CLASS IIB

LOVE IS IN

Panel 1: TEACHER HAS PHONED IN SICK, SO TODAY'S CLASS WILL BE TAKEN BY A STUDENT TEACHER . . .

Panel 2: A STUDENT TEACHER, EH?! / THIS'LL BE FUN! / OH, GOODY! / HEH! HEH! HEH!

Panel 3: HERE IS YOUR CLASS, MISS LUSCIOUS! / GOOD MORNING, EVERYONE!

Panel 4: JUST SIT YOURSELF DOWN! / WHY, THANK YOU! / LOOK! YOU'VE MISSED A BIT! / NO, I HAVEN'T! / COME BACK, CUTHBERT. ALL IS FORGIVEN!

Panel 5: NOW, WE'LL BEGIN TODAY'S MATHS LESSON WITH SOME LONG DIVISION. / YIPPEE! OUR FAVOURITE! / YEAH! WE LOVE LONG DIVISION! / SINCE WHEN?! / WELL, I'LL START YOU WITH SOME EASY ONE / TOOTS! WHAT ARE YOU DOING? / WHAT IT LOOKS LIKE

Panel 6: Finally, at home-time . . . / WELL, THANK YOU, EVERYONE, FOR BEING SUCH A GOOD CLASS! / HEY! DON'T MENTION IT! / CAN I CARRY YOUR BAG TO THE CAR, MISS?

Panel 7: And so . . . / HEY! STOP PUSHING AT THE BACK!

Panel 8: LOOK! THERE'S A STRANGE MAN IN YOUR CAR, MISS! / NO, NO, NO, DON'T WORRY KIDS, I KNOW / D'YOU WANT US TO SORT HIM OUT FOR YOU?!

MY! WHAT WELL-BEHAVED CHILDREN YOU ALL ARE!

OH, DEAR! I'LL HAVE TO CLEAN THE BOARD BEFORE I CAN BEGIN THE LESSON . . .

×4=16
×5=20
×6=24
E=mc²

WE'LL DO THAT, MISS!

YEAH! NO PROBLEM!

HEY! I WANT TO GO FIRST!

YOU CAN'T DO THAT!

HEY! LET ME GO!

CLASS! WHAT IS GOING ON?!?

25⟌600

ER . . . NOTHING!

. . . AFTER ALL, I'M GOING TO MARRY HIM IN JUNE!

Next morning . . .

TEACHER! YOU'RE BACK!

WHY, HELLO, TOOTS!

WHAT'S UP WITH EVERYONE? ARE THEY SICK?

YEAH! LOVE-SICK!

WHO WANTS TO BE A MILLIONAIRE?

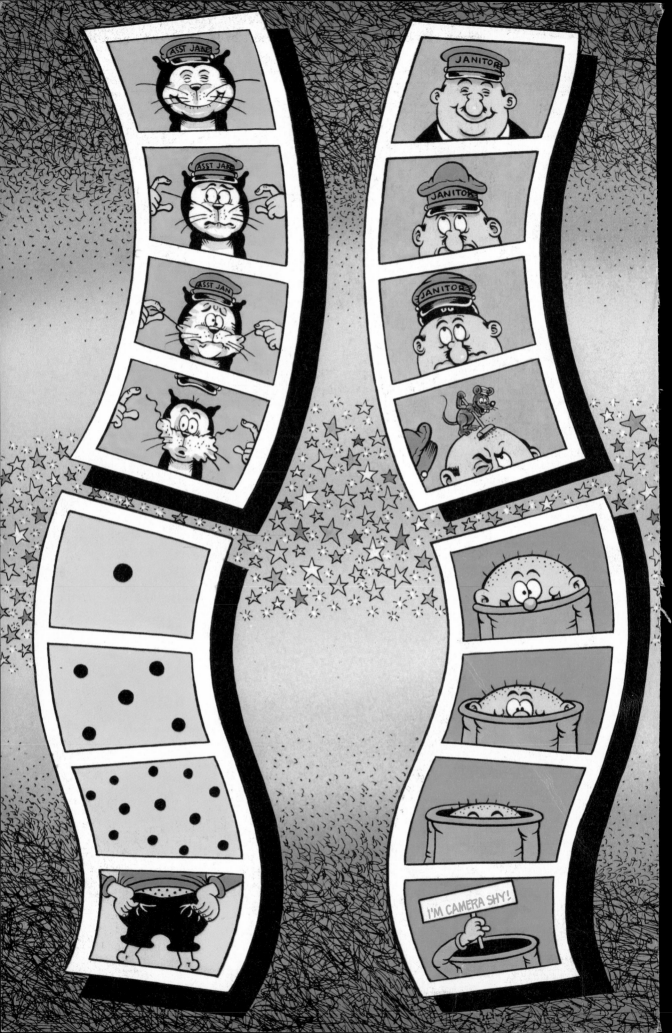